I choose

love

A JOURNAL of SELF-DISCOVERY:
Exploring love for yourself and the world

SARA HEPPNER

I CHOOSE LOVE
A Journal of Self-Discovery: Exploring Love for Yourself and the World

Canadian Intellectual Property Office | An Agency of Industry Canada

This book contains the ideas and opinions of its author. The intention of this book is to provide information, helpful content, and motivation to readers about the subjects addressed. It is published and sold with the understanding that the author is not engaged to render any type of psychological, medical, legal, or any other kind of personal or professional advice. The reader is responsible for their own choices, actions and results.

1st Edition. 1st printing 2021

Cover, Concept Design and Interior Design: Sara Heppner
Editor: Sara Heppner

ISBN: 978-1-7777598-0-3

Sara is an artist, a poet, a philosopher and a storyteller. I CHOOSE LOVE is a creative outpouring of her love and authenticity. Through her personal stories, thoughtful questions and gifted illustrations, Sara invites us on a journey of choosing love while unflinchinly confronting our shadows. This is a book to be read many times, and not just cover to cover. If you are feeling joy or sorrow, seen or invisible, curious or confused, open this book to any page and be informed and touched by Sara's wisdom. Sara helps us to see love in all it's fullness and to understand that we too can choose love.

Michele Hunt, Transformation Catalyst, Storyteller
Author of DreamMakers Books and film series

Full of the insightful thinking and wise musings of Sara Heppner, I CHOOSE LOVE is a precious gem, weaving her insights into a magical visual journey. This is a journal that brings goosebumps of joy and wonder as you move through the pages. A journal of the heart and soul. A journal you will never want to let go of.

Tracey Ezard, Speaker, Educator and Author of Ferocious Warmth

In her book I CHOOSE LOVE, you will receive the gift of Sara's being, her heart, her brilliance, and most of all, her love. This work required an untold amount of vulnerability, humility, and authenticity. She offers to all of us a call to action: to reflect, to dig deep, and to be a force for goodness in the world. I too choose love.

Darcy Winslow, Co-founder and Founding President, Academy for Systems Change

This beautifully illustrated journal is an invitation to all who choose love and want to explore their own heart in whatever way feels right — by writing, by drawing, by reading, by just being present to oneself. Sara's ability to communicate in color, pictures and words is a generous gift that sparks reflection and connection.

Kim Kita, Founding Member Magnolia Moonshot 2030

It is only with the heart that one can see rightly;
what is essential is invisible to the eye.

Antoine de Saint-Exupéry
The Little Prince

In deep gratitude to

my exquisite children Dalia, Nikki and Tessa
and my rock, Danny

who teach me to see with my heart every day

join me

This book has been brewing in me for years. Over a lifetime of finding my way in the world, I have amassed tidbits of "wisdom" that touch my soul. I am a deep listener, an intuitive thinker, a consummate connector and an incurable doodler. Doodling helps me think and make sense of my world. It helps me to connect my brain and my heart. I make marks EVERYWHERE - in my journals, in my books, on little pieces of paper scattered about the surfaces I inhabit in my everyday life. Sometimes they're messy and random. Sometimes they're clear and complete.

These are the tidbits that EMERGE from my SOUL

they remind me of HOW I WANT to be in the world.

And how I would like the world to be.

As a very private person, these musings were meant for me. About how to live a life of mindfulness and joy and love. I don't profess to know more than anyone else. Or that my way is the best way. Sometimes it works for me and sometimes it doesn't. I do know that the more OPEN I am to CURIOSITY and compassion, with myself and others, the easier it is to embrace ALL of ME. And build up the courage to share my musings with you.

There is no right way or wrong way to explore this journal. There is no beginning or end. It is meant to offer you opportunities for self reflection

INSPIRATION

discovery

joy creativity

To DISCOVER ♥ for YOURSELF

Ponder the questions...or don't.

Fill the white space....or don't.

Read it all at once or bit by bit...or don't.

Fold the pages, tear them out, scribble on them...or don't.

laugh   cry   rAGE   SMILe

SIT with your feelings   run from them.

N•O•T•I•C•E

Be

This is your JOURNEY, at your own speed, in your own way.

I hope that at least a tiny part of your soul is
sparked
at some point on this journey.

So that you can embrace all that is uniquely YOU

And bring the GIFT of your love into the world

You are not alone...

the LAW of KARMA:

You get to feel the way you make others feel

We sat across from each other ☐ a plexiglass wall separating us

We seemed the same...Two humans making our way in the world.
We chatted about the weather, Covid, working in new ways —
engaging in the small talk of conventional politesse.

Until I asked him about HIS story
and we looked into each other's eyes.

One searching for SAFETY. RELEASE.
the other for UNDERSTANDING. CONNECTION.

At first he said nothing.

And I RESPECTED that SPACE with compassion. no JUDGEMENT. no AGENDA. no ME. I listened with my soul while he bared his.

And then he FILLED
that SPACE with
HIS story first small and
tentative then
PAINFUL and STRONG
of a LIFE
lived in the
WRONG COLOR
for this PLACE
throughout TIME

Thank you for sharing, I said.

Thank you for asking.
I have never had a conversation
like this
with a white person.

Our eyes met again filled with tears
palm to palm
on that plexiglass window

Two humans creating
a world of possibility

I wish.......

My way is the only way I know...
It is not the only WAY.

Tell me about YOUR WAY.

Your way is the only way YOU KNOW...
It is not the only WAY.

I'll tell you about MY WAY.

And we will find OUR WAY.

Together.

yes

and...

Everyone
needs to be
HEARD

LISTENING
does not mean
AGREEING

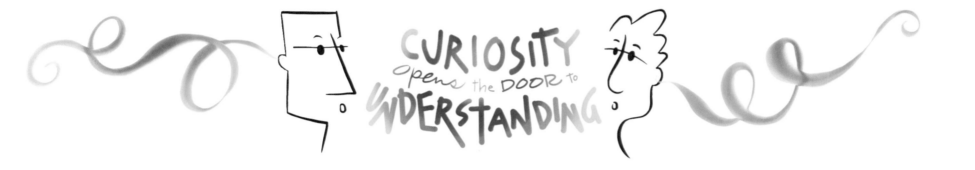

the ONE MINUTE RULE...

A conversation is an **EXCHANGE** between two or more people.

If you've been **TALKING** for more than one minute...

...SHUT UP!

It's time to give someone else a turn.

We learn more from listening than talking.

That's why we have 2 ears and 1 mouth.

We DO not have to
SPEAK
if we don't want to

We DO not have to
be SILENT
if we don't want to

Abundance • Ascension • Compassion

What if we all lived
from a place of
RESPECT

Love for ALL Beings

Difference • Curiosity • Acceptance

practice

WHAT
IS

oh... this is HOW it feels when...

• no JUDGEMENT.

• no S T O R I E S

• DROP IT!

STOP *and* NOTICE *what is happening*

LISTEN *to what you're* FEELING...
...your body is super-smart

SIT *with your* BODY *and be* CURIOUS

I never realized......

I'm ready to.....

Don't be AFRAID of DISCOMFORT

There is *light* in our DARK PLACES

FEAR can be PARALYZING.

FEAR can arise from the STORIES we CREATE.

FEAR can look like...

ANGER   Procrastination   Self Doubt   Busy-ness

HOW does FEAR show up in your life?   WHO is FEAR stopping you from being?

We HAVE
thoughts
and
emotions

they do
not
DEFINE
WHO
we are

FeeL them so you're
not VICTIM to them

Then let them
flow through you

and MOVE on...

How often do you say

I
AM
ANGRY

instead of

I AM
Feeling
ANGRY

You do **not** have to BE your emotions

I feel......

BEING WRONG

is a STATE that DEFINES who we are

DOING WRONG

is an action from which we can grow

create SPACE to

Let In

and

Let go

At the airport on a layover, again, waiting for my connection –
10 am ... too early for salad... or a turkey sandwich made five hours ago...
Walking back and forth and back and forth

deciding what to eat when I 👁 this woman ordering real hot porridge (she made sure it wasn't the INSTANT kind... yuk!)

I shared my appreciation for her genius as she sprinkled her own baggie of pre-washed blueberries which impressed me even MORE

At which point... for MY porridge!

...she gave me the rest of her precious blueberries comfort food, Once installed in my seat, I relished this most PERFECT hot because I love porridge and never eat it on an airplane, but because this random woman, a stranger, was happy to share her treasure with me.

most PEOPLE are GOOD

P·R·A·C·T·I·C·E

random
acts of
kindness...

...they make
the WORLD
a
Better place

REAL
OATMEAL

Comfort on the go

PAY ATTENTION

to the

DETAILS

of

life

Each precious moment only happens once.

Up at 4:30 am...again.
Busy brain eluding sleep... again.
That VORTEX of thoughts
feeding the **LUMP** in my chest

And then I remember to LOOK outside OF MYSELF

I see a beautiful soft light begin to fill the sky

Up in a tree a fiery cardinal greets the day with it's song. Another joins in. And then another.

As I sit in the glow of the rising sun and the sounds of a new day, I realize the lump has become a glimmer of possibility

And my early morning is a GIFT—

thank you
for
my spectacular
DAUGHTERS

thank you
for
love

Gratitude

- A felt sense of WONDER,
  THANKFULNESS

- APPRECIATION for LIFE

thank you
for
the JOY of
my grandchildren

thank you
for
LAUGHTER

thank you
for
this breathtaking
sunset

thank you
for
the WISDOM of
knowing when to be
silent

If you look, there are **BLESSINGS** in *all* that SURROUNDS YOU

thank you
for

thank you
for

What are you
Grateful
for?

thank you
for

thank you
for

There is no measure for gratitude.
the simple things are as important as the spectacular things...

What brought you

today?

If you can't think of anything, your day is not finished.

Did you know the average head weighs 10-11 pounds...
no wonder our thoughts can weigh us down.

TRUST your heart

BE in the moment

Get OUT of your head

I accept......

We do **not** have to be **PRISONER** to the **CRITIC** who *lurks inside*

I can
Have FAITH in
me

I can
Change
the
STORIES
that hold me back

I am WORTHY of
happiness

happiness comes in **MOMENTS**

it's **not** a PERPETUAL STATE

Did you know that

SMILING

actually stimulates a

chemical reaction

in your body?

serotonin

endorphins

dopamine

Sit quietly, close your eyes
and
TURN UP the CORNERS of your mouth

It actually lifts your spirit.

Try it!

Can I be
SATISFIED
with simply
BEING

We GROW in the direction of the QUESTIONS we ASK

Perhaps I am the
RIGHT ME
at the
RIGHT TIME
in the
RIGHT PLACE

When will we stop beating ourselves up for our "IMPERFECTIONS"?

We ALL have

unique gifts

What are yours?

I am……….

As I breathed in the trees and loud silence of the forest, I came upon a triad of trees that stood independent of each other,
            side by side.
        Each different in its
            shape,
                color,
                    texture.

From the other direction,
they stood TOGETHER as one. All their differences woven together. STRONG on their own and as ONE —

I see a tree standing TALL and beautiful covered in vines —

Is this the symbiosis of nature

Is one SUPPORTING the other?

Is one STRANGLING the other?

Is one LAUGHING?

The other CRYING?

LIVING OFF of the other?

Or perhaps they are simply BEING. together.

And what lies underneath...

the silent connections of roots and funghi and microscopic tendrils
that nurture the existence of this magnificent system.
The seen and the unseen woven together
pushing and pulling in blissful harmony

Who are we to defy nature...when we are nature?

Did you ever **wonder** ·········

the SPACE BETWEEN thought and

reaction IS WHERE YOU FIND YOUR SELF

Remember to P·A·U·S·E and

There are so many reasons to be

BUSY

If I'm not busy,
people will think
I'm lazy...

Better take
care of that
right away...

Doing "nothing"
is boring...

Doing "nothing"
feels selfish...

My to-do list
is so long,
I can't stop
now...

I don't want to
waste my time...

If I don't
feel like doing this,
I'd better
do something else...

Trouble is...most of them are
imposters of PRODUCTIVITY

Rather than be BUSY

Just BE.

After all... we are human BEINGS not human doings.

Why........

I know · · . . .

What do you do when you can't SLEEP...

When your BRAIN can't stop and you go down that chattering rabbit hole

When I need to get out of my head,

I go into my BODY

Close my eyes

Breathe

Tilt my head to one side

And turn it so slowly to the other side that it's barely moving

Back and forth in a slow-motion rhythm

Focusing on that quiet smooth energy

How my neck moves

the rhythm

the connection

the calm

close your eyes

take a breath

there it was...this GIANT pile of dark, luscious earth waiting to be discovered. And there was the little boy, anxious to explore the world around him.

He threw himself in that pile of dirt with COMPLETE abandon

...squeezing the earth through his little fingers

...watching how it stuck and fell apart

...squealing with delight as he fell face first...dirt filling his ears, snot bubbles of dirt inflating and deflating

...feeling that luscious moisture on his hot little boy hands

as he breathed in and out

Not a care in the world as he discovered all he could about this fantastic pile of wonder.

Filled with joy

Completely in the moment

As his adults watched,
they revelled in his *joy*

and it GREW.

As the neighbours walked by,
they basked in his *joy*

and it GREW.

the MAGICAL thing about *joy* is it's *contagious*

Why do we FORGET to

as we get OLDER?

What brings you *joy* ...feels GOOD... yes?!

Do something that brings you *joy* EVERY DAY... you *deserve* it.

So there I was waiting to board the train amidst the array of everyday people going about their business.

At the head of the line was a young family with three little boys in tow. Energy in check as they behaved as they were told.

Just like all the others in line.

Until they handed their boarding passes to the agent.

POW!

This man looked at each of them straight in the eye, addressed them by name and SHARED his incredible ENERGY with them.

Off they went BOUNCING down the platform.

The most amazing thing was that EVERYONE in line was smiling too. All of a sudden, the dull station was shining bright.

This agent continued to share his beautiful energy with every passenger.

He could have checked everyone in the way most agents do...with a cursory smile and the required "Welcome". Instead, he CHOSE to CONNECT with each person and bring some light into their day.

EVERYTHING we DO and SAY
affects those around us.

What ENERGY would you like to spread around the world?

When we LOOK UP from our devices
we can

connect

with other HUMANS...

...the way we're meant to.

I see........

WHO do YOU CARE about

WHO CARES about YOU

The only person who
has to take care of you

...is YOU.

Asking for HELP is a form of SELF CARE

I am willing to be **vulnerable**

I accept that I can't do this myself

I am **not** stupid or **weak**

I want to **learn**

there is **no shame** in asking for help

...even if I need help...
I CAN **love** MYSELF

What can you do to take *better care* of YOURSELF?

let go of

SELF JUDGMENT

TRYING

the CRITIC in ME

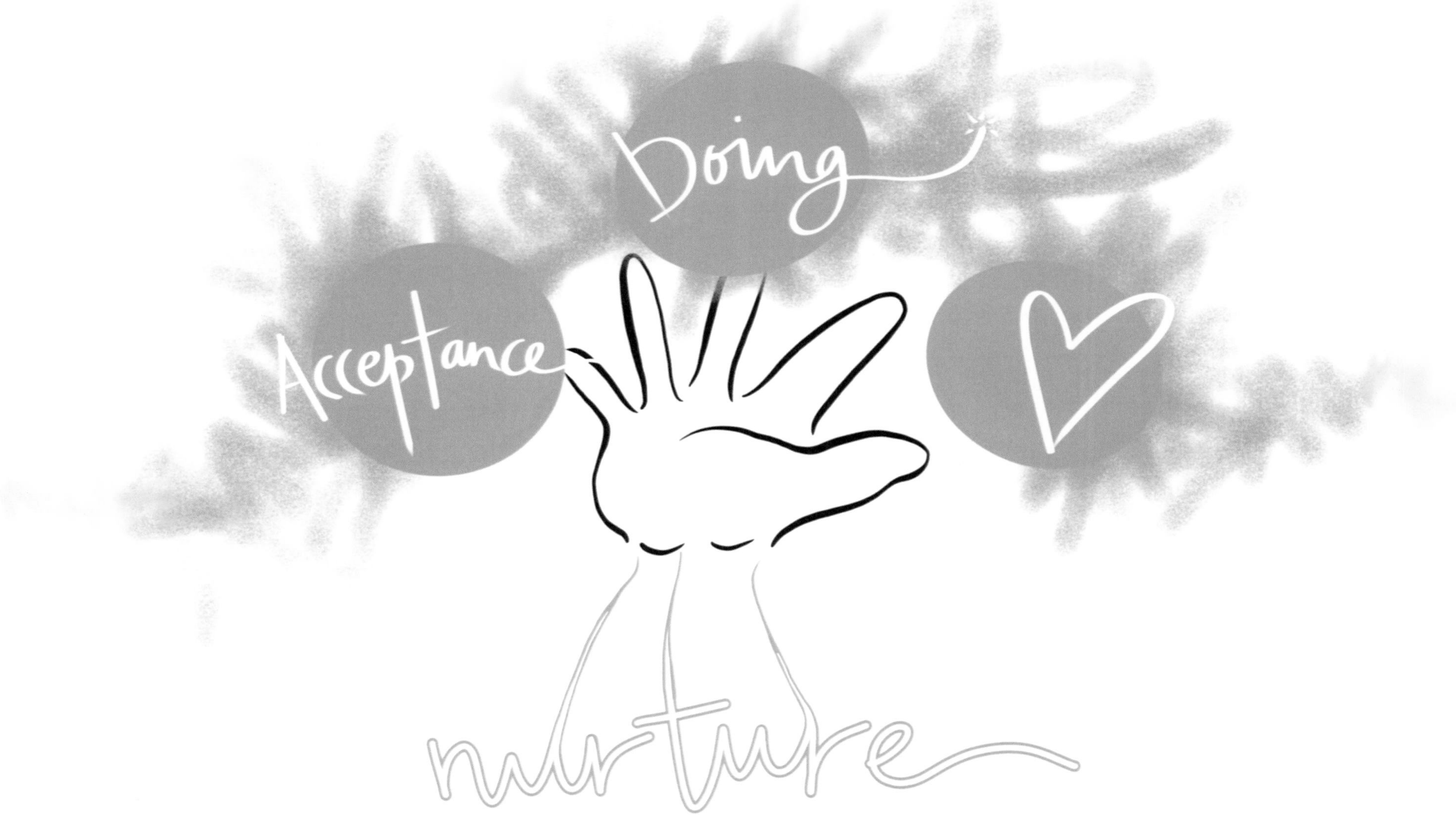
Doing
Acceptance
nurture

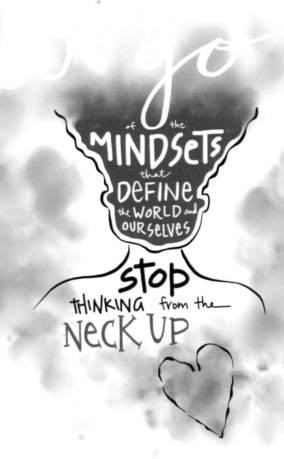

WHO is *they* and WHY do we CARE?

WHO could YOU BE if you *didn't listen*?

Why try to fit into a square

When you don't have to FIT into ANYTHING—

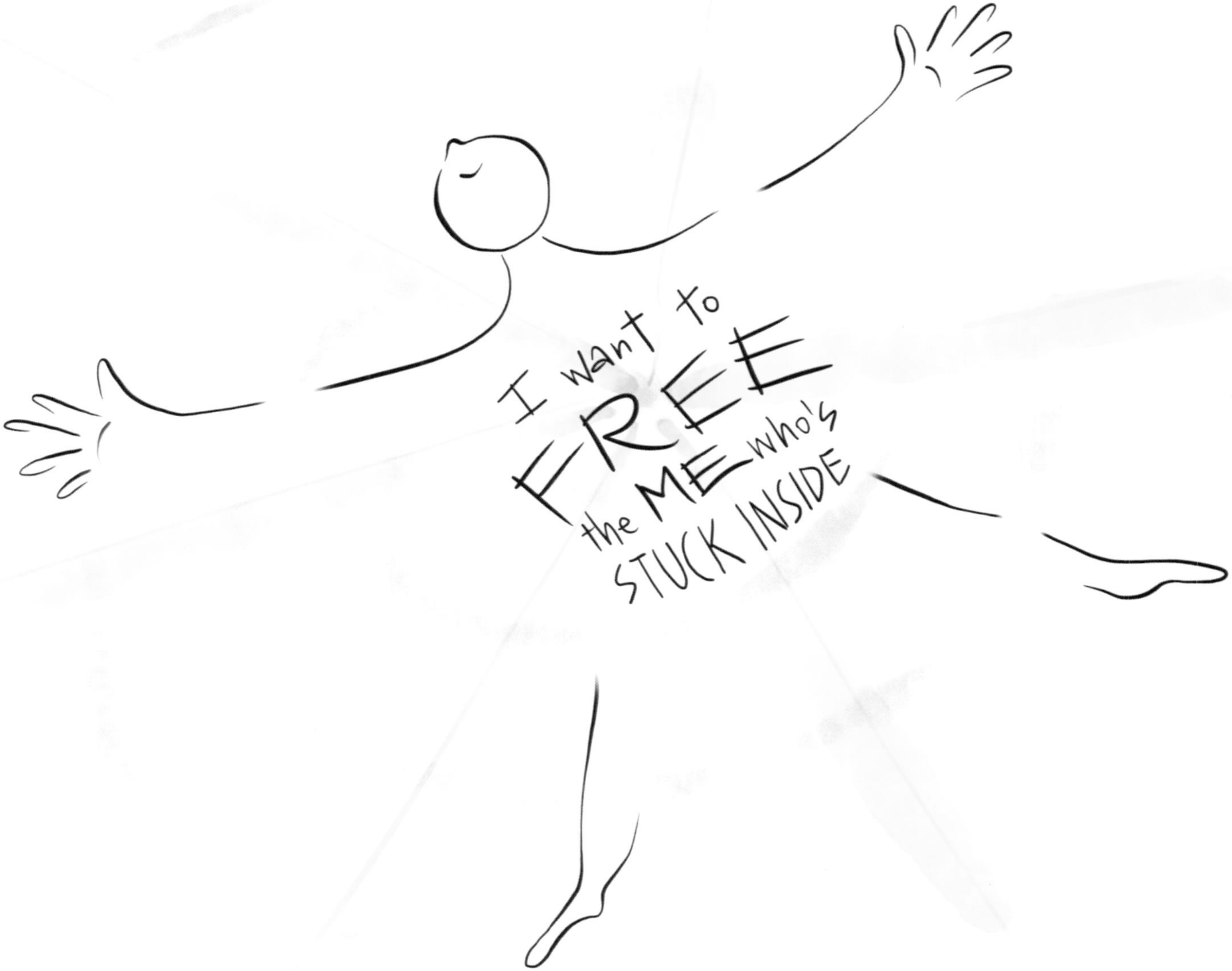
I want to
FREE
the ME who's
STUCK INSIDE

It's TIME to create your OWN STORY!

YOU are the
AUTHOR of your LIFE

YOU have the
POWER to CHOOSE
the STORIES that serve you
and
the STORIES that don't

Trust that
YOU KNOW YOURSELF
Best

Some are
so deeply
planted we
can't get
RID of THEM

You never FINISH what you start

You're so CREATIVE

Yes I can

You're so SELF-CENTERED

You're so calm

Some we GET RID OF

I'm so STUPID

I am not ENOUGH

You never TELL me anything

You never get MAD

Some we LIVE UP TO even if they're not TRUE

You're too much

I'm so UGLY

You always SMILE

You never SMILE

You're so SMART

You're so Kind

Some we choose to KEEP

Have you noticed that the more you do something,
the easier it gets?

Maybe that's because you begin to change the stories you tell yourself...

I CANNOT

Funny how we take on different personas
depending on where we are and who we're with.
Even ourselves.

STORIES follow us through our lives about
WHO WE ARE
and
HOW WE NEED to BE

What stories do you need to r e l e a s e

The only PERSON you NEED to BE is YOU —

It takes couRAGe to use our VOICE and say NO.

It's also
EMPOWERING.

What do YOU need to
say NO to?

With RESPECT...

I can't......

I can......

"SHOULD"

SAYS WHO?

let
go of

SELF-SABOTAGE

GUILT

need for
PERFECTION

they are a CHOICE

CHOOSE

desire

instead of

REQUIREMENT

I would LIKE TO...

I COULD...

I hereby GIVE MYSELF Permission to...

LISTEN to your HEART

...even if it's scary...

Who said we have to be

P·E·R·F·E·C·T

We are ALL

doing our

BEST

that is ENOUGH

How does it feel when you're trying to be
the BEST?

think of a time when your BEST
was ENOUGH.
How did it feel?

EVERYTHING in life is a
CHOICE

our
ACTIONS

our
INACTION

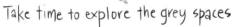

Take time to explore the grey spaces

our
REACTIONS

You have the POWER to choose HOW to LIVE your life.

I choose ......

Why waste our energy on

a PAST we cannot CHANGE OR a FUTURE we cannot CONTROL

when

ENERGY ARISES in the PRESENT

Today I am *grateful* for...

what does *love* mean to you?

love

is a

VERB

It requires Action

It's always
Changing

We have to **Do** it to **Feel** it

Love is even **BETTER** when it's **shared**

• COLOUR these in
and
• Tell the recipient WHY you LOVE them

• Be SPECIFIC

• CUT them out

• SHARE them.

♥ Send one to YOURSELF

♥ Send one to someone who NeeDS some TLC

♥ Send one to Someone... JUST BeCAuSe

♥ Send one to someone UNSUSPECTING

Don't worry about being perfect... cuz neither is love.

I CHOOSE

love

What do YOU choose?

Sara Heppner seeks to find balance by living from her head *and* her heart. Her passion for creative communication comes from a lifetime of formal artistic training, highly focused listening, and a belief in the need for connection. A graphic designer by training and a graphic facilitator by profession, she captures the essence of dialogue in a highly visual format thereby enhancing cooperation, inspiring creativity, and enabling co-creation.

A lifetime of travel has allowed Sara to immerse herself in cultures around the world. Regardless of the context and the stories of their history, she is touched by a common thread: the unmet need for connection and love. Sara partners with individuals and groups to help them think and act on a human level; in their personal lives, professional environments, and in the global community. Her focus is on building collaborations that nurture socio-economic, ecological, and spiritual well-being across all walks of life.

Sara is a faculty member of The Academy for Systems Change and a founding member of Magnolia Moonshot 2030, a women's initiative to create a world where all can flourish. She has had the privilege of working with clients across many sectors both locally and internationally, including education, healthcare, government, consulting and not-for-profit. She is most excited to engage in women's empowerment, leadership, human rights and systems change initiatives.

By approaching life with an open heart and focusing on love, Sara believes that together, we can make the world a better place.

Sara Heppner shares her empty'ish nest in Montreal, Canada with her prince-of-a-husband and their dog and cat. Whether near or far, her children and grandchildren are the light in her soul.

Wanna know more? Visit www.saragrafix.com

Peek · a · boo!····.